COLDPLAY   X&Y

D0243719

Wise Publications
part of The Music Sales Group

London / New York / Paris / Sydney / Copenhagen / Berlin / Madrid / Tokyo

Published by
Wise Publications,
8/9 Frith Street, London, W1D 3JB, England.

Exclusive distributors:
Music Sales Limited,
Distribution Centre, Newmarket Road, Bury St Edmunds,
Suffolk, IP33 3YB, England.

Music Sales Pty Limited,
120 Rothschild Avenue, Rosebery,
NSW 2018, Australia.

Order No. AM92113
ISBN 0-7119-4239-0
This book © Copyright 2005 by Wise Publications,
a division of Music Sales Limited.

Management by Estelle Wilkinson and Dave Holmes.

Music arrangements by Derek Jones.
Music processed by Paul Ewers Music Design.
Edited by Lucy Holliday.
Original Design and Art Direction: Tappin Gofton.
Photography: Kevin Westenberg, Tom Sheehan and Coldplay.

Printed in the United Kingdom.

www.musicsales.com

SQUARE ONE

Words & Music by Guy Berryman, Jon Buckland, Will Champion & Chris Martin

The fu-ture's_ for dis-co-ver-ing___

the

space in which we're tra - vel - ling.

From the top___ of the first page___
The first line of the first page___

10

2. Un - der the sur - face try - ing to break through.

De - ci - pher - ing the codes in you.

I need a com - pass, draw me a map.

I'm on the top, I can't get back.

D.S. al Coda

(Oh,_____ oh.)_____

It does-n't mat-ter who you are.

Ooh.___

You just want_____ some-bo - dy

Is there a - ny - bo - dy out____ there who____ is lost and hurt and lone - ly too,____ are they bleed - ing all____ your col -

WHAT IF

Words & Music by Guy Berryman, Jon Buckland, Will Champion & Chris Martin

WHITE SHADOWS

Words & Music by Guy Berryman, Jon Buckland, Will Champion & Chris Martin

Oh,_____ oh._____

May - be you'll get___ what you want - ed,___ may - be you'll stum - ble up-

-on it.___ Ev-'ry-thing you_ ev - er want - ed_ in a per - ma - nent_ state._

May - be you'll know_ when you've seen it,___

FIX YOU

Words & Music by Guy Berryman, Jon Buckland, Will Champion & Chris Martin

Tune guitar down a semitone

1. When you try____ your best but you don't suc - ceed,____ when you get_____ what you want but not what you need,____ when you feel____ so tired but you can't sleep,____

TALK

Words & Music by Guy Berryman, Jon Buckland, Will Champion,
Chris Martin, Karl Bartos, Ralf Huetter & Emil Schult

to talk to you.

You could take a pic-ture of
(3°) don't know where you're go-ing and you

some-thing you see.__
want to talk.__

You

In the fu-ture where will I be?__
feel like you're go-ing where you've been be-fore.__

38

And they're talk - ing it____ to me.____

D.S. al Coda

So you

Coda I

some - thing that's nev - er been done.____ Do____

some-thing that's nev - er been done.____

X&Y

Words & Music by Guy Berryman, Jon Buckland, Will Champion & Chris Martin

Try-ing hard to speak and fight-ing with my weak hand, dri-ven to dis-trac - tion, it's

all part of the plan. When some-thing is bro - ken and you try to fix it,

try - ing to re-pair it a - ny way you can.

and sing- ing_____ ooh._____

Ooh._____

SPEED OF SOUND

Words & Music by Guy Berryman, Jon Buckland, Will Champion & Chris Martin

1. How long be-fore I get in,_____ be-fore it_____
2. Look up, I look up at night,_____ pla-nets are mov-
3. I-deas that you'll ne-ver find,_____ all the in-ven-

All those signs,___ I knew what they meant. Some things you can't in-vent. Some get made___ ___ and some___ get sent.___ Ooh._____ And

birds go fly-ing at the speed of sound_ to show you how it all be-gan._

Birds_ came fly-ing from the un-der-ground,_ if you could

see it then you'd un-der-stand._ Ah, when you see it then you'll un-der-stand._

A MESSAGE

Words & Music by Guy Berryman, Jon Buckland, Will Champion & Chris Martin

62

LOW

Words & Music by Guy Berryman, Jon Buckland, Will Champion & Chris Martin

1. You see the world in black and white, no co-
2. The sky could fall, could fall on me, the part-
3. You see the world in black and white, not paint-

- lour or light.
- - ing of the sea.
- - ed right.

You think you'll nev - er get it right but you're wrong,
But you mean more, mean more to me than a - ny co -
You see no mean - ing to your life,

To Coda I

64

65

You should try._____

You should try._____

THE HARDEST PART

Words & Music by Guy Berryman, Jon Buckland, Will Champion & Chris Martin

wish that I could work it out.___

Oh, and I,___

73

I won-der what it's all a-bout.____

won-der what it's all a-bout.____

76

SWALLOWED IN THE SEA

Words & Music by Guy Berryman, Jon Buckland, Will Champion & Chris Martin

TWISTED LOGIC

Words & Music by Guy Berryman, Jon Buckland, Will Champion & Chris Martin

first time ri - vers will run.

2. Hun - dreds of years in the fu - ture
(3.) - at - ed, then drilled and in - va - ded.

You'll go back - wards but then you'll go.

3. Cre -

You'll go

back - wards_____ but then you'll go for - wards_____ a - gain._

3° Instrumental

_____ You'll go back - wards_____ but then you'll go

1, 2, 3.

for - wards._____ You'll go

4.

TILL KINGDOM COME

Words & Music by Guy Berryman, Jon Buckland, Will Champion & Chris Martin